ANNIVERSARY CLOCK ADJUSTING

by

Mervyn Passmore

Copyright notice
First published 2002

© Mervyn Passmore 2002
ISBN 0 907109 01 2

All rights reserved. No part of this book may be reproduced or transmitted in any form or by any means whatever without the written permission of the publisher, with the sole exception of the 'Beat scale' and the 'Setting up and regulating leaflet' at the back. This beat scale and leaflet may be reproduced, but only for the personal use of the reader.

Every effort is made to make sure that all publications are accurate and that the information given in them is correct. However, information can become out of date and errors and ommisions are possible. Standard working practices, tools and substances can become considered unsafe. This book is therefore sold on the condition that neither the author nor publisher can be held legally responsible for the consequencies of any error, ommission or recommendation.

Acknowledgements
The Horolovar Company, Box 264 St. Clair Shores, Michigan MI 48080 USA. Publishers of 'The Horolovar Repair Guide'.

Illustrations by Ben Stevenson

Published by
Mervyn W. Passmore
1 Ellen Street
Portslade
Brighton
East Sussex BN41 1EU England

ANNIVERSARY CLOCK ADJUSTING

To Niki and her friends, without whose help this book would never have been finished.

Contents

Chapter 1	Before adjusting anything	1
Chapter 2	Letting down the mainspring	3
Chapter 3	The suspension wire	5
Chapter 4	How they work	9
Chapter 5	Setting up the clock	15
Chapter 6	Escapement adjustments	23
Chapter 7	Regulation	33

Introduction

Anniversary or 400 day clocks were originally marketed as gifts. Many were given as wedding or birthday presents that could be wound ceremoniously on each subsequent anniversary. They are still given on this basis, but somehow ceremoniously changing the battery doesn't seem to have the same sensation!

A mechanical clock mechanism that will run for over a year without being wound either has to have a disproportionately large mainspring, or be a delicate piece of precision engineering. You can see the mainspring barrel is no bigger than a conventional clock, so they fall into the latter category. As a consequence of only having a standard type of mainspring, everything about them is designed to be as frictionless as possible. Even the hands are lightweight. The glass dome is there to prevent draughts as well as dust from affecting the mechanism.

The design is quite different to conventional clocks, and this can cause clockmakers to dislike them. Lacking the experience and understanding of this style of mechanism can result in frustration and faults.

This book reveals the workings and adjustments clearly and concisely. There are drawings to cover almost every part of the process of adjusting. Technical information has been kept to a minimum. Complex drawings of escapements and teeth often don't help the in a practical situation. With this book you learn by doing the adjustments. As you do them, you will begin to understand the principles of these delicate and ingenious mechanisms.

Learn by doing

The first time you use the book, follow it through from the start. It doesn't take long to follow all the instructions. The beat scale is particularly important to use and understand. After you have used the book, you will find that clocks which always seemed to stop or give trouble will work as if they were new.

Chapter 1

Before adjusting anything

There is a wealth of information already published on repairing conventional clocks, and repairing Anniversary or 400 day clocks is no different in most respects. They need cleaning, pivoting, bushing, lubricating and general repairs just like any other clock. Because they run for over a year between windings, the movements must be as frictionless as possible and generally in good condition - but no more so than a fine Vienna Regulator or carriage clock. If you are happy with the condition of the mechanism or 'train' in general, any problem you may have could be an adjustment.

However, the adjustment of these clocks can present the repairer with difficulties. The concept of the rotary or 'torsion' pendulum is so unique in clockmaking that few of the familiar standard principles apply. The time taken for an adjustment to be verified can also be infuriating - it can take several minutes for the clock to stop, even when quite out of beat.

They have also got a bad reputation for timekeeping, mostly because they get wound only once per year. Their weekly or monthly-going counterparts are often corrected for minor timekeeping errors subconsciously by the owner at every winding. A year going mechanism has each week's error accumulated to the last, and so it gets further

Check the movement over thoroughly

and further out. Eventually it is so far out it gets considered unreliable!

Before even considering adjustments, check the movement thoroughly for wear, lubrication and strength of mainspring. Remember that many of these clocks are left for long periods, even years, with the mainspring tightly wound. Indeed, the first thing done by each person who attempts to 'get it going' is to give the key yet another turn if possible. The spring can remain so tightly wound for so long it can lose some of its all-important strength. Congealed lubricant on the spring can also bind the coils, and a clock is often more likely to go when needing a few turns than when wound to the maximum. Better timekeeping adjustments are also achieved with a spring less than fully wound.

Letting down the mainspring

Chapter 2

Letting down mainsprings

If the mainspring is very tightly wound, let some of the tension off it now.

Select a strong steel key that accurately fits the winding arbor.

Holding the movement in one hand, take up the tension of the spring with the key and gently ease the spring loaded click away from the ratchet wheel. Allow the key to rotate about a quarter to half a turn and release the click. Ensure that the click has engaged in the ratchet before releasing the key.

Releasing some spring tension

Repeat the process two full turns from the fully wound position. Keys with side wings have less chance of

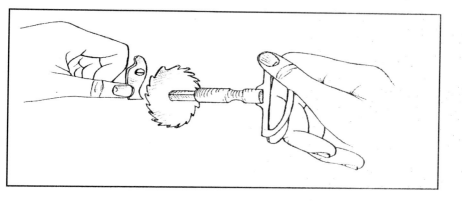

Take great care!

slipping, so never use carriage clock keys for this. The best type of key to use is a conventional steel key.

Great care should be taken when carrying out this task as one mistake can destroy a finger as easily as a clock. Let-down keys are purpose made tools to control the letting down of springs. By having a key attached to a handle, the speed of rotation can be controlled by how tightly it is held.

A typical set of let-down keys

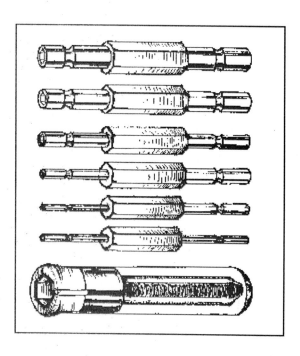

Chapter 3

The suspension wire

The torsion suspension wire causes more grief and heart-ache to repairers than any other part of these clocks. Too thick, too thin, too long or short, steel or phosphor bronze. But always to blame! To understand the problem fully we first need to look at the history of the suspension wire.

Some of the old trademarks used by the major German manufacturers.

Anniversary clocks as we know them emerged towards the end of the nineteenth century. The United States was the favourite target for sales, and huge quantities were exported there and to the UK by German firms such as Gustav Becker, Jahresuhren-fabrik and Kieninger & Obergfell. German factories either made their own suspension wires or bought them from German specialists. The materials used by early models were phosphor bronze

The Horolovar replacement wires

The kind of drawing used by the 400 Day Repair Guide to identify models

alloys. These were very prone to changes in temperature. The diversity of models and the differences in wires also caused great difficulty for early repairers, having to stock or get wires specific to each model, even when many of them used identical parts.

In the 1950's the American 'Horolovar Company' began selling their new nickel steel alloy wires. These wires were a considerable improvement on the original phosphor bronze units and the German clock manufacturers began to use them themselves. They were particularly attracted by the low co-efficient of expansion of the material used. Phosphor bronze got considerably longer with increases in temperature, whilst this 'Invar' type of alloy hardly increased in length at all. Phosphor bronze got so much longer in warm weather that the clocks were almost always slow in summer. The consistency of the material characteristics and wide range of sizes combined with the Horolovar 'Suspension Spring Guide' helped repairers select and fit new wires more easily than ever before. The Guide showed line drawings of backplates together with details of the wire to use, and the current '400 Day Repair Guide' remains in this same style today but with much more information than these early editions. The use of the Guide to select a unit or wire

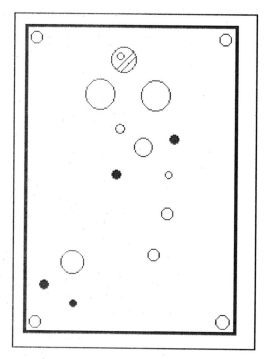

The suspension wire

still depends on the clock having its original pendulum. This is an important factor to consider, as many have been switched by unscupulous dealers over the years.

Replacement wire thicknesses

The range of wires currently available

The principle behind the wires and the Guide was to make a full range of thicknesses available - so many, that almost every clock could be catered for without any modification being needed. There was no magic behind this - a reduction of 0.0001" (.0025mm) in thickness will change the timekeeping by about 3 ½ seconds per minute. A change in length of ¼" (6mm) alters the timekeeping by about a further second. Changing the pendulum adjustment from one extreme to the other has an average effect of 4 seconds per minute. So, by calculated use of one of these wires combined with the pendulum adjuster, almost every clock was covered.

Thicknesses of torsion wire

.0018"	.046mm	.0033"	.084mm
.0019"	.048mm	.0034"	.086mm
.0020"	.051mm	.0035"	.089mm
.0021"	.053mm	.0036"	.091mm
.0022"	.056mm	.0037"	.094mm
.0023"	.058mm	.0038"	.097mm
.0024"	.061mm	.0040"	.102mm
.0025"	.064mm	.0045"	.114mm
.0028"	.071mm	.005"	.127mm
.0030"	.076mm	.0055"	.140mm
.0031"	.079mm	.006"	.152mm
.0032"	.081mm		

The Guide was essential if the repairer was to rapidly select the right wire, even if the original was still available. The characteristics of the Phosphor-bronzes and the nickel steel were different. All metals vary in their characteristics. For example, a wire of lead would stay wherever it was put. A mercury wire would be a puddle on the base! Likewise Phosphor Bronzes and Nickel Steels vary, so you cannot simply measure the original and fit another of the same physical dimensions. As there is no easy way to measure the characteristics of the original without laboratory

Varying materials have varying characteristics

equipment, the Guide remains one of the principal ways of selecting a wire. Since it was written, the author of this book has published 'Anniversary Clock Identification' which simplifies the selection of the correct wire. The web site mentioned inside the back cover of this book also provides a link to a free interactive online movement identification system devised and written by the author.

However, an assortment of wires and a little patience will achieve the same. You simply make an educated guess at the thickness and fit the wire. Substitution up or down will soon get it right. The wrong wire won't stop the clock, unless you are using one that is totally inappropriate. Provided you are using a wire of about 0.004" for a standard clock and about 0.0025" for a miniature model, the only symptom will be a gain or loss.

The wrong wire won't stop the clock

Before you look closely at timekeeping, it makes sense to establish that the clock will go for more than just a few minutes without stopping. If you are changing the wire or unit, you naturally need to pick the right one. But don't blame it for everything! Adjust the clock properly in terms of beat, rotation etc. so it runs consistantly. If it then fails to keep time, you can then look at the torsion wire in greater detail. If it stops, there is probably a weak mainspring or a loss of power somewhere in the train. Conventional clock repairing skills apply to the movement itself, and it will need overhauling.

How they work

Chapter 4

A simplistic view of a clock

Assuming everything from the mainspring through to the escape wheel is in reasonable condition, we can go on and set the clock up. But first you must understand the theory of torsion pendulums. Not an in-depth knowledge of angles and momentum, but just the basic principles of operation.

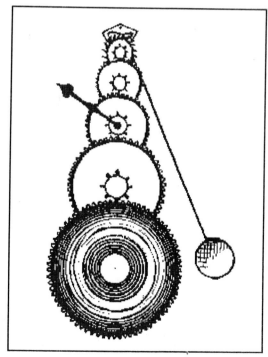

A clock can be said to consist of 'a wound spring with hands attached via a set of gears, trying to unwind as fast as possible but only able to do so by a small amount with each vibration of a pendulum'.

The power of the spring is used to impart a small quantity of energy to keep the pendulum swinging. Both Anniversary and conventional clocks have a train of wheels going from the mainspring to the escape wheel. Both have levers connected to the escapement.

Conventional clocks

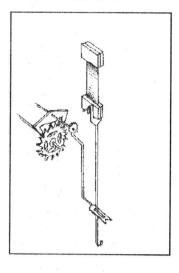

A conventional clock

A conventional clock has a vertical lever (the crutch) connected to the escapement, which incorporates a two pronged fork through which the pendulum rod hangs.

In order to tick, this fork must move from side to side far enough to let the escape wheel teeth 'escape'. The natural frequency of the pendulum controls the time between the ticks. The pendulum normally allows the lever to oscillate between 1 to 3 times a second.

400 day clocks

A 400 day clock has a vertical lever (the impulse pin) connected to the escapement. This pin has the two prongs (tines) of a fork enclosing it, and this fork is clamped to a thin wire strip. In order to tick, this fork must move from side to side far enough to let the escape wheel teeth 'escape'. Each time the fork moves from side to side, the strip must twist. The further up the pin the fork is located, the more degrees the fork (and also the torsion wire) must twist. The pin on most older clocks oscillates once every 7.5 seconds.

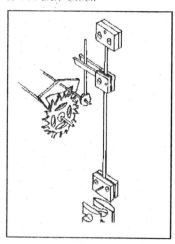

A 400 Day Clock

Important differences

There are several important facts that emerge from careful study of these two differences.

A conventional clock has little that can be adjusted:
The weight of the pendulum is fixed.
The position of the fork (yoke) is fixed.
The shape of the bob is fixed.
The thickness of the suspension wire has very little bearing on the timekeeping of the bob.

All that can effectively be changed by adjustment is:

1. The pendulum length.

Conventional clock adjustments

The longer the pendulum drop, the slower the clock goes.

2. The pendulum beat.
The clock is in beat when the swing to one side is equal to the swing to the other.

3. The pallet drop and locking.
It is essential that the pallets are correctly located in relation to the escape wheel teeth.

400 Day clock adjustments

A 400 day clock has many possible adjustments.

1. The position of the fork on the wire.
The higher the fork up the lever, the greater the degree of twist required. If this is too high, the twist may require more energy than is available and stop the clock. If too low, so little twist may be required that unwanted ticks (flutters) can occur while the torsion wire is near the mid-point.

2. The effective diameter of the pendulum.
This is effected by expanding the adjustable balls or weights on the bob. The further out the weights, the slower the clock will go.

3. The length of the wire.
The longer the pendulum suspension wire, the slower the clock will go. This has the least effect of the adjustments and is limited by appearances and the base.

4. The pendulum beat.
The clock is in beat when the swing in one direction is equal to the swing in the other.

5. The pallet drop and locking.
It is essential that the pallets are correctly located in relation to the escape wheel teeth.

6. Torsion wire strength.
In the ordinary way, the thickness of the torsion wire is fixed. In practice though, this is frequently replaced during a service. The new wire may be different to the original. ***The thicker the wire, the faster the clock goes***. This can easily be visualized by imagining an extremely

How they work

thick wire. The bob would rapidly return to the mid point. A fine, delicate spring would take ages to return to that same point.

14　　　　　　　　　　　　　　　　　Anniversary Clock Adjusting

Setting up

Chapter 5

Keeping it ticking

It is very important to make the adjustments to these clocks in the right order. There are some points that must be correct to start with, and these are easily established.

Before making major changes

Centre the pendulum adjuster.

Put the balls or pendulum weights in the mid-point of their adjustment in and out. You can use them later for final timekeeping adjustment either way.

Place the base on a firm level surface.

If adjustable feet are fitted, use them to ensure the bob hangs directly over the centre of the base.

Check the gap between the fork and impulse pin.

The gap between the tines of the fork and the impulse pin is very important. This should be as little as possible, but enough to ensure it does not bind. The most likely position for binding will be at the point of maximum rotation. At this point, the tines are still horizontal, but the effective width of the pin has increased, being at an angle. Too much gap will result in lost power and make escapement flutter more likely.

16 Anniversary Clock Adjusting

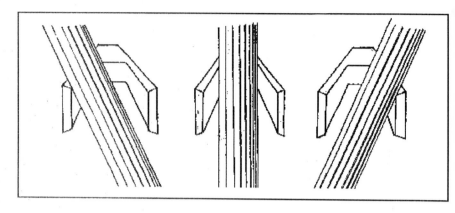

Check the gap between the tines and the impulse pin at the extremes as well as in the central position.

Put the pendulum in beat.

The clock is in beat when the number of degrees of rotation from the stationary mid-point to a 'tic' is the same as the number of degrees from the mid-point to a 'toc'.

To check and adjust the beat, start by photocopying the beat scale at the back of the book. You will also find a useful guide on 'Setting up and Regulating'. You can photocopy both these for your own private use. You may want to leave a copy of the setting up leaflet with the clock for future reference. Additional packs can be purchased separately for commerial use from the publishers.

The beat scale consists of a circular printed scale and five marker arrows.

Using the photocopy, cut around the outside of the circle. Remove the shaded area if a pendulum locking device will obstruct the scale. Now cut out the five marker arrows.

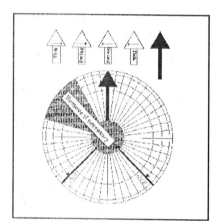

The rotaton scale at the back of the book

Setting up

Tape the black arrow to the pendulum.

Tape the large black arrow in any convenient place on the pendulum. It will be easiest if you tape it near the front, as adjustments are most easily made at the back of the clock, and this is where the arrow will be swinging to when the clock is running.

With the clock stopped and the pendulum quite still, place the scale beneath the pendulum, with the black arrow aligned with the arrow secured to the pendulum. Secure it in place with more masking tape. If you have had to cut out the centre of the scale to avoid any pendulum locking device, be sure to tape down the edge.

Align the two black arrows and tape the scale in position.

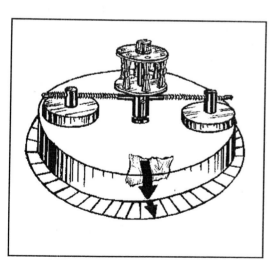

Now rotate the pendulum no more than 1 1/2 whole turns and let go gently. Allow the clock a few minutes to settle down.

The reason for the four remaining paper markers is to help keep a note of four points during rotation.

The two 'swing' markers are to show the maximum distance the black arrow swings, clockwise and anticlockwise.

Place the 'swing' markers at the extremes of swing in each direction.

The position of the 'tick' markers show the two points during the swing when the escapement ticks.

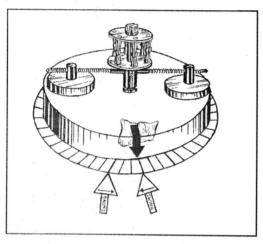

Start by putting the 'swing' markers in position. Make sure you use the correct ones, referring to the direction indicators printed on them. This will help on clocks with more than a full turn of rotation. Simply use the marker with the direction arrow showing the direction of rotation. Put them at the point when the pendulum stops and begins its return.

The 'tick' markers are not so easy to place, as you need to look in two places at once! Watch the escape wheel, or listen very carefully for the sound, and put the 'tick' markers exactly at the point the ticks occur.

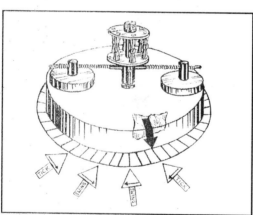

Place the 'tick' markers where the ticks occur.

Setting up

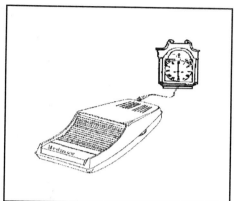

An electronic beat amplifier is a great help with this job. They generally have a delicate crystal pickup connected to an amplifier. The pickup senses the mechanical vibration of the ticks, which is then amplified. However, just by watching a few turns of the pendulum, you will soon be able to place the markers by eye.

An electronic beat amplifier

Note the position of the four markers on the scale. At this stage we are not concerned with the amount of rotation, but the 'Tics' and 'Tocs' and the maximum swings should be an equal distance from the fixed black arrow on the scale. If they are not the same, the saddle that supports the top block must be rotated slightly. The actual rotation required is very small and is best done with a beat setting tool. This can remain fitted to the saddle while adjustments are made. Because of its length, very small changes can be made. However, you can make the adjustments with any smooth jaw pliers or other clamp arrangement.

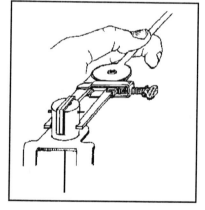

Using a beat setting tool to rotate the saddle.

If the clock is out of beat, you will see a difference between the amounts of overswing. Overswing is the distance between the tick marker and its corresponding swing marker. If badly out of beat, one direction may have no overswing at all, and this is what makes a clock stop. The slightest vibration, extra friction in the train, a sticking mainspring, and the pendulum will not make it to the tick position.

Anniversary Clock Adjusting

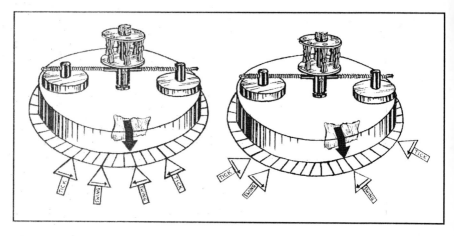

Clocks in and out of beat

No tick means no impulse energy back, so next time there is even less chance of a tick.

This is all because the wire is biased towards one tick more than the other.

Use the rotation scale markers

Make small adjustments to the saddle, and move the four markers around accordingly. The saddle (not the tail of the tool) has to be rotated in the direction of the marker with the least overswing.

Trial and error will soon get the ticks and swing equal. Leave the scale and markers in position. You will need them later to check the amount of rotation.

Don't be surprised if, next morning, the overswings have increased considerably. This is the sign of a properly adjusted and free running clock.

Setting up

Flutter occurs when the pendulum passes its mid-point and the fork is too low.

Check the height of the fork.

If you have purchased a new suspension unit, the fork height should be correct. There is no specific 'correct point' that can be easily described, but it must be high enough to stop flutter at the central position. Flutter occurs when the fork is so low down the pin that hardly any twist of the torsion wire occurs between ticks. As the fork passes the mid-point, one or more extra ticks can take place. This often accounts for mysterious and rapid gain in timekeeping when everything seems correct. If too high, it will prevent the escapement from working properly and stop the clock. It may be some time before the clock actually stops, as the extra momentum given it by you to start it can take some minutes to disappear.

Check the amount of rotation.

Using the same scale as before, watch how far round the black arrow rotates from the mid-point to the 'tic' and 'toc' markers.

Use a rotation scale

These, if you have completed the beat setting procedure, will now be equal. 270 degrees is the standard rotation, but more will not normally be a problem. Up to 1 ¼ turns is fine. Less than 270 degrees normally means the clock will stop after a while. To increase the rotation raise the fork slightly, provided this does not interfere with the

Use the scale to check the amount of rotation

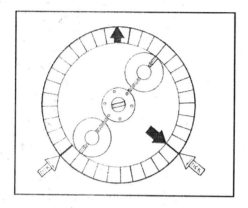

proper operation of the escapement action. If that fails to increase the rotation sufficiently, there is a loss of power somewhere. The pendulum is not getting the impetus needed to give it a healthy turn. Check the gap between the tines of the fork again. Too much gap allows the pin to move without actually pushing the fork. Go back and check the whole train. Look for hands that are too tight, a sticky mainspring etc.

The rotation from the mid-point to a 'tic' must be the same as from the mid-point to a 'toc'

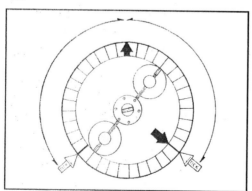

Chapter 6

The escapement

This is the point in many technical books that suddenly uses words you have never heard before combined with complex diagrams. This publication isn't like that. However, there are some words you should learn. For example, rather than continually using phrases like 'the gap between the inside face of the escapement pallet that lets teeth into the anchor and the rear face of a tooth just let in', we'll use 'entry drop'. We will look at these names later. If you want to know more about the fascinating variety of escapements that have been invented over the years and how they work, there are many specialist books on the subject.

In the meantime, you must decide what kind of escapement your clock has.

Dead Beat or Pin Pallet?

Dead Beat or Pin Pallet?

400 Day clocks generally have either pin pallet or dead beat escapements. The simplest and quickest way to decide is just to look for wire pins on the pallets! If you have pins touching the escape wheel teeth, you have a pin pallet clock; anything else, whether it be a solid pallet or an adjustable one, will be dead beat.

Both types have two pallets, one called the entry and the other the exit. This is easily remembered by visualizing the small group of teeth that are enclosed by the pallets.

Typical pin pallet and dead beat escape wheels and pallets.

One pallet allows teeth to enter the group (the entry pallet) while the other allows them to exit.

The Graham Dead Beat escapement

The dead beat escapement was invented by George Graham, and is called dead because the escape wheel stays dead still while the teeth are locked on the pallet surface, even when the pallets are still moving. To visualize this better, look at a standard longcase second hand. This is normally connected directly to the escape wheel arbor, and you will note how it recoils back slightly with every tick. A dead beat equivalent displays only a forward motion, stopping dead still at each seconds marker.

This was the first type of escapement used on 400 day clocks, and is ideal for their use. It maintains an almost constant turning force on the wire.

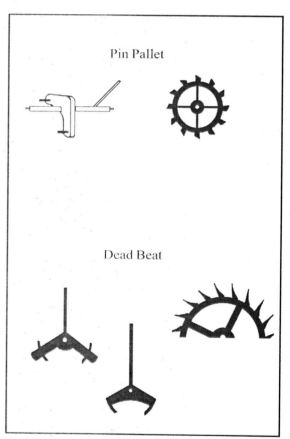

Escapement adjustments

The fixed pallet (left) and the adjustable type.

There are two types of pallets used, a fixed pallet fashioned from solid steel and an adjustable one using removable pallets (nibs). The principle of operation is the same for either type. The adjustable type has pro's and con's. Admittedly they can be adjusted to compensate for wear, sometimes be reversed and are easily removed for attention, but they can cause more problems than they solve. They are too easily altered by well-meaning amateurs on a trial and error basis in the hope it will fix a problem.

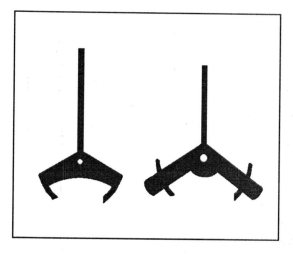

Inspection holes in the backplate.

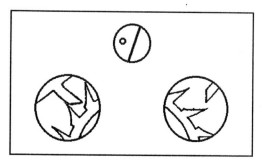

The adjustment of the escapement is important to a 400 Day clock, and later manufacturers provided inspection holes in the back plates to help. Through these holes we can see the various criteria we need to check.

Entry and exit pallets.
The entry pallet shown on the left allows teeth to enter into the enclosure. The exit pallet on the right allows them out.

As with most other adjustments on these movements, it helps if opposites are equal. The entry pallet's 'tic' will always relate to one direction of rotation, and the exit pallet's 'toc' refers to the other. Their respective 'drops' need to be checked, and adjusted to be as equal as possible. The entry and exit drops are shown in the illustrations.

The entry & exit drops should be equal.

The entry drop is the distance the tip of the tooth about to enter the enclosure has to travel when it drops onto the entry pallet.

The entry drop.

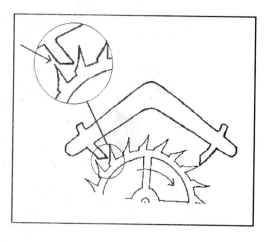

The exit drop is the distance the last tooth tip has to travel when it hits the surface of the exit pallet.

With the pendulum removed, look through the inspection holes if you have them while moving the impulse pin from side to side with a finger.

Escapement adjustments

The exit drop

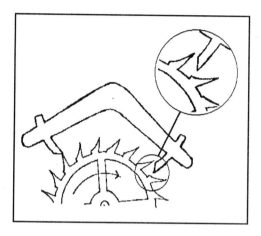

Watch the action of the pallets and teeth. The two drops should be as equal as possible.

Raising the pallets decreases the entry drop and increases the exit drop.

Lowering the pallets increases the entry drop and decreases the exit drop.

There are three methods of altering the height of the pallets. On some models the pivot is supported by an eccentric nut set in the backplate, while others use the position of the suspension bracket. To alter the eccentric nut, use an off-set screwdriver with the blade adjusted to fit the slot accurately. Only make the smallest changes possible, and check the operation of the escapement as you do it.

On less expensive clocks, the pivot is sometimes on an adjustable arm.

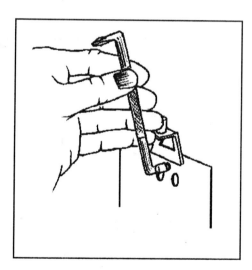

Altering the pivot height when fitted with an eccentric nut.

Marks scribed around the suspension bracket by a previous repairer.

The types that use the position of the suspension bracket to control the height of the pallet arbor need to be set carefully after each dismantling, while their counterparts can normally be stripped and re-assembled without any change to the drops occurring. You may find a previous repairer has scribed around the suspension bracket to aid re-assembly.

Now take a look at the illustrations showing the two locks.

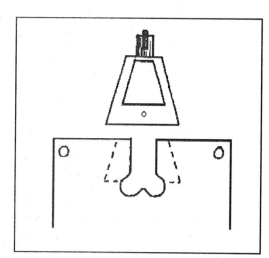

The entry lock is the depth of contact between the entry pallet and the tooth about to enter the enclosure.

The exit lock is the depth of contact between the exit pallet and the tooth about to leave the enclosure.

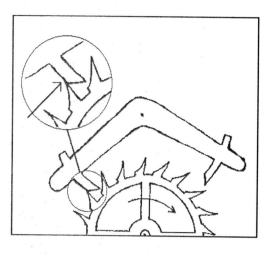

With the pendulum removed, observe the locking distances. These should also be as large as possible without causing any risk of jamming on any of the teeth. They should also be equal.

The entry lock.

Escapement adjustments

The exit lock

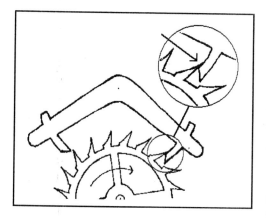

Lowering of either or both of the adjustable pallets (nibs) or the pallet arbor will increase the locking, and vice versa.

The raising or lowering of either or both of the individual nibs or the pallet arbor will have no effect on any locking imbalance.

The only way to alter the amount of locking is to alter the angle or shape of the pallet faces.

Adjusting the pallets will not cure locking imbalance.

This is extremely unlikely to be needed, and once done there is no going back. Some models had reversible double-ended nibs, and these can easily be verified.

The method of adjusting the faces is deliberately not explained here - you are strongly urged not to do this unless you are very confident they need it. The surfaces are very hard and brittle. The process is described in almost all clock repair books.

Pin Pallet Escapements

These were introduced much later on in the history of the 400 day clock, and are much less expensive to manufacture. They have proved very successful on small and miniature models.

Typical pin pallets and wheel.

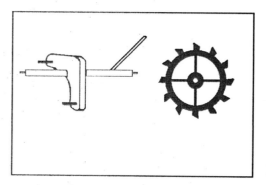

One major advantage to the pin pallet escapement is the robust shape of the escape wheel. Gone are the vulnerable points to the teeth, as the flat outer surface is the one that makes most contact with the pallets. The pins are fixed so there is generally little to adjust. On most movements they will snap off if bent. They should be at right angles to the pallet. If they have been bent by a previous repairer, you must try to straighten them. Use as little force as possible, and try to move them just once. Broken pins can be replaced with pivot steel. Taper the end of the steel, having first selected a piece of similar diameter. It can be pushed firmly into the original hole.

Do not attempt to bend the pins.

The drop and locking must be checked in the same manner as the Graham escapement, although the points to look for differ.

The entrance and exit drops are checked for equality by eye, again moving the impulse pin from side to side manually. If necessary, the eccentric nut is rotated so as to effectively raise or lower the pallets.

Escapement adjustments 31

As with the Graham escapement:

Raising the pallets decreases the entry drop and increases the exit drop.

The initial pin pallet drop.

Lowering the pallets increases the entry drop and decreases the exit drop.

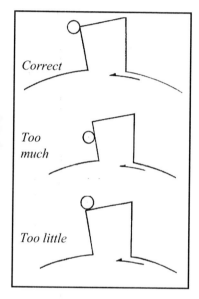

Correct

Too much

Too little

The initial locking of the pin onto the undercut back of the tooth should be $1/2$ its diameter. This is fixed in manufacture and unless the pins are bent or damaged, will still be the same.

As the escapement continues to lock, the pin will be drawn down the undercut side of the tooth, and lock in the bottom corner. Because the tooth is undercut at an appropriate angle, it offers no resistance to the pin when it lifts. As soon as the pin lifts above the undercut edge, the lifting surface along the top provides the impetus to the pendulum.

The locking sequence

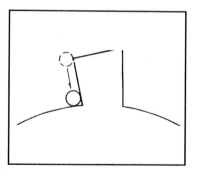

If the clock won't keep going after all these procedures (regardless of timekeeping), go back through them all again. You may have missed something, but more likely, you may have made some alteration that has affected a previous adjustment. The suspension controls timekeeping, but is most unlikely to be so far out in thickness to actually stop the clock.

Regulation

Chapter 7

Keeping time

Now check the timekeeping. This sounds like the first thing you would do, and you probably already have. However, there is little point in trying to rectify timekeeping problems unless you are sure everything else is in order. After all, if the clock will not run successfully for any length of time, it hardly matters if it keeps time or not!

Provided the suspension unit is the correct strength and length, you should get reasonable timekeeping straight away. To make the clock go slower, turn the bob adjuster to make the balls or counterweights move further out. If, despite your adjustments, the clock will not keep the right time, you must now look more closely at the suspension wire itself.

The strength and length of the wire combined with the shape and weight of the bob control the natural frequency of the pendulum as a whole. Your pendulum will oscillate at a certain natural frequency whether there is a clock or not. Obviously it will soon stop on its own, without that impetus from the escape wheel. If the clock goes consistently fast or slow without stopping or fluttering, the problem almost certainly lies with the wire. There is also the possibility that the bob is not the original one.

You can easily establish the number of beats per minute your clock should make. Remove the bob and use your finger to manually operate the escapement. Count how many ticks are required to move the minute hand 5 minutes. Divide the result by 5 and round your answer to the nearest whole number. You should get a result of 8 beats per minute for a standard clock, 10 for miniature models and possibly more for modern movements.

Now replace the bob and check the number of rotations per minute. Compare this with your calculated value. This timing has nothing to do with the operation of the clock and will give the same result if you turn the suspension unit around so the fork faces backwards. It is the rotary equivalent of Galileo's pendulum and the timing is fixed by the thickness of the wire and the mass of the bob.

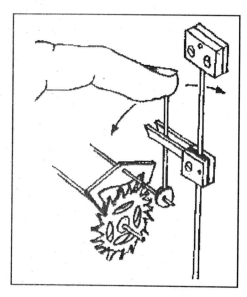

Manually operate the escapement to count the beats per minute

If the actual beats per minute is more than your calculation, the clock is going too fast - adjust the pendulum weights to be as far out as possible. If this fails to slow the beats per minute enough, fit a thinner suspension.

It it goes too slowly, (but consistently so, not just as a prelude to stopping), fit a thicker suspension spring.

Regulation

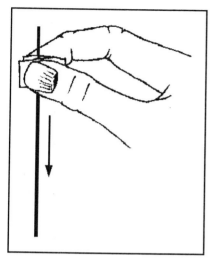

Thinning a wire with abrasive paper.

You can thin down a suspension with fine abrasive paper. Fold a piece of 1200 grit abrasive paper and hold it either side of the wire with your thumb and finger. Hold one end of the wire with smooth jaw pliers. Wipe the folded abrasive paper down the wire firmly. Treat the whole length of wire evenly, and remember that each time you pass the abrasive over the wire it is equivalent to a reduction of about 0.0001" (.0025mm). Go carefully; you can take more off but you can't put any back!

When you have the correct suspension in place and the clock is running well, make adjustments to the bob's weights or balls in an orderly manner. The further out the balls or weights, the slower the clock will run. Like any pendulum adjustments, make them only at regular intervals, and give the bob a chance to settle down between changes. Apart from the early alterations, a change once every 24 hours is soon enough. Write down the degree of adjustment you make and the effect it has - that way you can quickly calculate how much is needed to get it almost spot-on in just a few days.

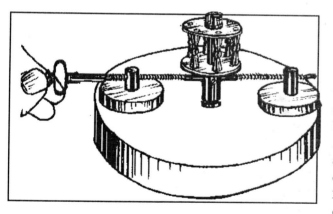

Adjust the weights or balls to alter the timekeeping.

There is no doubt that timekeeping alters as the spring unwinds, just like any other clock that does not benefit from a fusee barrel. To get the best result, give them a bit of a wind during the year. This is preferable to altering the bob as the year progresses.

Conclusion

It will only have taken you a short time to go through the adjustments described in this publication, and if you have done them carefully and in the right order the clock will be set up better than it probably has been for decades.

You will have learned that 400 day clocks are not the frustrating and baffling mechanisms portrayed by so many repairers, but carefully designed timepieces capable of going over 50 times longer per winding than the majority of others. They are often elegant, inexpensive, fun to watch and just as good at timekeeping as other clocks.

All you need do now is spread the news of your new found expertise. Sit back and they will be brought to your door in droves.

Points to remember

The thicker the suspension spring, the faster the clock will go.

The further out the balls or counterweights, the slower the clock will run.

The higher the fork, the greater the rotation.

The change in timekeeping from the slowest to the fastest positions on the pendulum adjuster is normally 4 seconds per minute.

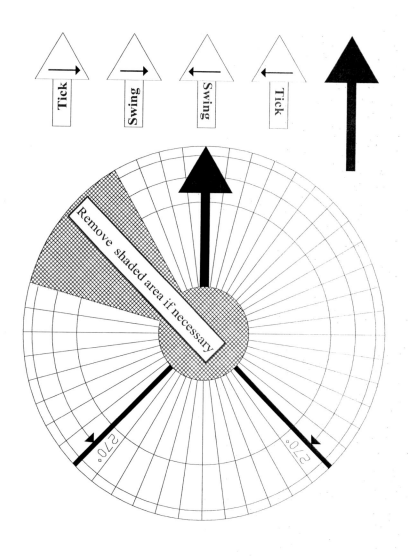

Adjusting scale. © Mervyn Passmore 2002

42 Anniversary Clock Adjusting

SETTING UP & REGULATING
ANNIVERSARY CLOCKS

It is essential a clock is 'set up' properly when put into operation after a move to a new position. No matter how thoroughly a clock is overhauled, if it does not receive this final attention it may suffer from loss of power and subsequently stop. Provided a clock is transported carefully with the pendulum removed or secured and subsequently placed on a firm level surface, no adjustment should be necessary.

Siting
A clock capable of running a year between windings has a delicate mechanism and is very susceptible to vibration or knocks. The slightest sideways movement can stop a clock. **Always site anniversary clocks on a solid surface like a mantelpiece or shelf, never a table.**

Regulation
A number of factors affect the timekeeping of a clock (temperature, balance etc.). No matter how well a clock may have been overhauled, final adjustment is almost always necessary. A rotary pendulum has a fixed length, unlike a conventional clock. Although length does affect the timekeeping, adjustments are made by moving the balls or pendulum weights in and out. Ball type pendulums normally have a serrated adjustment nut and this is often marked 'Fast - Slow' or 'Advance - Retard'. This moves all the balls in and out simultaneously. Older clocks often had a flat disk pendulum with a pair of weights connected by a steel shaft. These are adjusted by rotating the shaft that connects them using a small key. This makes both weights move in and out simultaneously. **The further out the balls or weights, the slower the clock will run.**

Do not alter the pendulum more than once in 24 hours and remember that spring driven clocks may run slower as the spring unwinds. Keep a note of the amount of adjustment made and the resulting effect.

The reputation anniversary clocks have for poor timekeeping is generally unfair. Weekly wound clocks tend to be corrected weekly for any small loss or gain. Because anniversary clocks require no attention for months on end, the error accumulates unnoticed until it becomes unacceptable. A well regulated clock with a modern temperature compensating suspension should keep good time.

Never move a clock with the pendulum attached, as this will damage the delicate spring on which the pendulum is suspended and may cause expensive damage to the escapement.

Setting up

The pendulum
The variation in design of anniversary clocks makes it impossible to give precise instructions on all models, but they fall into two main categories:
Detachable pendulums: The pendulums of these older and simpler clocks are completely removed for transport. Very carefully fit the pendulum onto the brass block at the bottom of the suspension wire. If a suspension wire guard is fitted, then this sometimes has to be raised (by loosening any nuts or by friction alone) to get access to the bottom block. Never put any strain on the wire as you fit the pendulum. The hook normally goes up and over the pins projecting from the sides of the block. Ensure that the bottom of the pendulum fits within any guide on the base.
Attached pendulums: Later models have locking devices to allow the clock to be moved with the pendulum in place. Various methods have been used, but almost all involve levers that hold and release the pendulum securely. Gently release the lever

Levelling
Later clocks have levelling screws. Adjust these until the pendulum hangs quite centrally. If no levelling screws are fitted, check the surface beneath the clock with a spirit level and ensure the pendulum hangs centrally. A poor but functional method of levelling is to use two small cardboard wedges under the base.

Starting and Stopping
Start by rotating the pendulum in either direction one complete turn from the stationary position and let go. It will rotate slightly faster than normal, but will gradually settle down to about 3/4 of a turn each way. Never turn the pendulum more than 1 1/2 turns*, as this may put a permanent twist in the wire, rendering it useless. To stop the clock, gently grasp the pendulum as it approaches the central position

Exceptions:
Although known as anniversary clocks (the intention being to wind them on a particular anniversary each year), some models go for 1,000 days and at least one cheap model only goes for a month.
*Some very modern clocks rotate quickly, with up to 3 revolutions each way.

Further supplies available from most clock material dealers or direct from Meadows & Passmore Ltd. 1 Ellen Street Portslade Brighton East Sussex BN41 1EU
© Meadows & Passmore Ltd, 1997

INDEX

400 Day clock adjustments 12
Amount of rotation 21
Beat amplifier 19
Beat setting tool 19
Beats per minute 34
Conventional clock adjustments 11
Dead beat escapement 24
Eccentric nut 27
Entry drop, dead beat 26
Entry drop, pin pallet 31
Entry lock, dead beat 28
Entry lock, pin pallet 31
Escapement 23
Exit drop, dead beat 26
Exit drop, pin pallet 31
Exit lock, dead beat 28
Exit lock, pin pallet 31
Gap between fork and impulse pin 15
Height of the fork 21
Flutter 21
History 5
Horolovar Company 6
How they work 9
Inspection holes 25

Insufficient rotation 22
Invar 6
Keeping it ticking 15
Keeping time 33
Let-down keys 4
Letting down mainsprings 3
Locking distances 28
Locking imbalance, dead beat 29
Nibs 29
Overswing 20
Pallets 25
Pendulum adjustment effect 7
Phosphor bronze 6,7
Pin pallet escapements 30
Putting in beat 16
Replacement wire thicknesses 7
Rotaton scale 16
Suspension, thinning 35
Suspension wire 5
Swing markers 17
Tick markers 18
Trademarks 5
Varying materials characteristics 8
Wrong wire won't stop the clock 8

Anniversary Clock Adjusting. Appendix/removable pages

Appendix

The pages that follow have been duplicated so that you can remove them from the book and use them for clocks that you have adjusted.

The scales are a duplicates of page 41.

The setting up leaflets are duplicates of pages 43/44.

You may also photocopy these pages for your own personal use. You may not copy any part of this book for commercial purposes.

Further copies are available from the publisher in packs of 25.

Anniversary Clock Adjusting Appendix/removable pages

SETTING UP & REGULATING
ANNIVERSARY CLOCKS

It is essential a clock is 'set up' properly when put into operation after a move to a new position. No matter how thoroughly a clock is overhauled, if it does not receive this final attention it may suffer from loss of power and subsequently stop. Provided a clock is transported carefully with the pendulum removed or secured and subsequently placed on a firm level surface, no adjustment should be necessary.

Siting

A clock capable of running a year between windings has a delicate mechanism and is very susceptible to vibration or knocks. The slightest sideways movement can stop a clock. **Always site anniversary clocks on a solid surface like a mantelpiece or shelf, never a table.**

Regulation

A number of factors affect the timekeeping of a clock (temperature, balance etc.). No matter how well a clock may have been overhauled, final adjustment is almost always necessary. A rotary pendulum has a fixed length, unlike a conventional clock. Although length does affect the timekeeping, adjustments are made by moving the balls or pendulum weights in and out. Ball type pendulums normally have a serrated adjustment nut and this is often marked 'Fast - Slow' or 'Advance - Retard'. This moves all the balls in and out simultaneously. Older clocks often had a flat disk pendulum with a pair of weights connected by a steel shaft. These are adjusted by rotating the shaft that connects them using a small key. This makes both weights move in and out simultaneously. **The further out the balls or weights, the slower the clock will run.**

Do not alter the pendulum more than once in 24 hours and remember that spring driven clocks may run slower as the spring unwinds. Keep a note of the amount of adjustment made and the resulting effect.

The reputation anniversary clocks have for poor timekeeping is generally unfair. Weekly wound clocks tend to be corrected weekly for any small loss or gain. Because anniversary clocks require no attention for months on end, the error accumulates unnoticed until it becomes unacceptable. A well regulated clock with a modern temperature compensating suspension should keep good time.

Never move a clock with the pendulum attached, as this will damage the delicate spring on which the pendulum is suspended and may cause expensive damage to the escapement.

Setting up

The pendulum

The variation in design of anniversary clocks makes it impossible to give precise instructions on all models, but they fall into two main categories:

Detachable pendulums: The pendulums of these older and simpler clocks are completely removed for transport. Very carefully fit the pendulum onto the brass block at the bottom of the suspension wire. If a suspension wire guard is fitted, then this sometimes has to be raised (by loosening any nuts or by friction alone) to get access to the bottom block. Never put any strain on the wire as you fit the pendulum. The hook normally goes up and over the pins projecting from the sides of the block. Ensure that the bottom of the pendulum fits within any guide on the base.

Attached pendulums: Later models have locking devices to allow the clock to be moved with the pendulum in place. Various methods have been used, but almost all involve levers that hold and release the pendulum securely. Gently release the lever.

Levelling

Later clocks have levelling screws. Adjust these until the pendulum hangs quite centrally. If no levelling screws are fitted, check the surface beneath the clock with a spirit level and ensure the pendulum hangs centrally. A poor but functional method of levelling is to use two small cardboard wedges under the base.

Starting and Stopping

Start by rotating the pendulum in either direction one complete turn from the stationary position and let go. It will rotate slightly faster than normal, but will gradually settle down to about 3/4 of a turn each way. Never turn the pendulum more than 1 1/2 turns*, as this may put a permanent twist in the wire, rendering it useless. To stop the clock, gently grasp the pendulum as it approaches the central position.

Exceptions:

Although known as anniversary clocks (the intention being to wind them on a particular anniversary each year), some models go for 1,000 days and at least one cheap model only goes for a month.

*Some very modern clocks rotate quickly, with up to 3 revolutions each way.

Further supplies available from most clock material dealers or direct from
Meadows & Passmore Ltd. 1 Ellen Street Portslade Brighton East Sussex BN41 1EU
© Meadows & Passmore Ltd, 1997

Anniversary Clock Adjusting. Appendix/removable pages   v

SETTING UP & REGULATING
ANNIVERSARY CLOCKS

It is essential a clock is 'set up' properly when put into operation after a move to a new position. No matter how thoroughly a clock is overhauled, if it does not receive this final attention it may suffer from loss of power and subsequently stop. Provided a clock is transported carefully with the pendulum removed or secured and subsequently placed on a firm level surface, no adjustment should be necessary.

Siting

A clock capable of running a year between windings has a delicate mechanism and is very susceptible to vibration or knocks. The slightest sideways movement can stop a clock. **Always site anniversary clocks on a solid surface like a mantelpiece or shelf, never a table.**

Regulation

A number of factors affect the timekeeping of a clock (temperature, balance etc.). No matter how well a clock may have been overhauled, final adjustment is almost always necessary. A rotary pendulum has a fixed length, unlike a conventional clock. Although length does affect the timekeeping, adjustments are made by moving the balls or pendulum weights in and out. Ball type pendulums normally have a serrated adjustment nut and this is often marked 'Fast - Slow' or 'Advance - Retard'. This moves all the balls in and out simultaneously. Older clocks often had a flat disk pendulum with a pair of weights connected by a steel shaft. These are adjusted by rotating the shaft that connects them using a small key. This makes both weights move in and out simultaneously. **The further out the balls or weights, the slower the clock will run.**

Do not alter the pendulum more than once in 24 hours and remember that spring driven clocks may run slower as the spring unwinds. Keep a note of the amount of adjustment made and the resulting effect.

The reputation anniversary clocks have for poor timekeeping is generally unfair. Weekly wound clocks tend to be corrected weekly for any small loss or gain. Because anniversary clocks require no attention for months on end, the error accumulates unnoticed until it becomes unacceptable. A well regulated clock with a modern temperature compensating suspension should keep good time.

Never move a clock with the pendulum attached, as this will damage the delicate spring on which the pendulum is suspended and may cause expensive damage to the escapement.

Setting up

The pendulum
The variation in design of anniversary clocks makes it impossible to give precise instructions on all models, but they fall into two main categories:
Detachable pendulums: The pendulums of these older and simpler clocks are completely removed for transport. Very carefully fit the pendulum onto the brass block at the bottom of the suspension wire. If a suspension wire guard is fitted, then this sometimes has to be raised (by loosening any nuts or by friction alone) to get access to the bottom block. Never put any strain on the wire as you fit the pendulum. The hook normally goes up and over the pins projecting from the sides of the block. Ensure that the bottom of the pendulum fits within any guide on the base.
Attached pendulums: Later models have locking devices to allow the clock to be moved with the pendulum in place. Various methods have been used, but almost all involve levers that hold and release the pendulum securely. Gently release the lever.

Levelling
Later clocks have levelling screws. Adjust these until the pendulum hangs quite centrally. If no levelling screws are fitted, check the surface beneath the clock with a spirit level and ensure the pendulum hangs centrally. A poor but functional method of levelling is to use two small cardboard wedges under the base.

Starting and Stopping
Start by rotating the pendulum in either direction one complete turn from the stationary position and let go. It will rotate slightly faster than normal, but will gradually settle down to about 3/4 of a turn each way. Never turn the pendulum more than 1 1/2 turns*, as this may put a permanent twist in the wire, rendering it useless. To stop the clock, gently grasp the pendulum as it approaches the central position.

Exceptions:
Although known as anniversary clocks (the intention being to wind them on a particular anniversary each year), some models go for 1,000 days and at least one cheap model only goes for a month.
*Some very modern clocks rotate quickly, with up to 3 revolutions each way.

Further supplies available from most clock material dealers or direct from
Meadows & Passmore Ltd. 1 Ellen Street Portslade Brighton East Sussex BN41 1EU
© Meadows & Passmore Ltd. 1997

SETTING UP & REGULATING
ANNIVERSARY CLOCKS

It is essential a clock is 'set up' properly when put into operation after a move to a new position. No matter how thoroughly a clock is overhauled, if it does not receive this final attention it may suffer from loss of power and subsequently stop. Provided a clock is transported carefully with the pendulum removed or secured and subsequently placed on a firm level surface, no adjustment should be necessary.

Siting

A clock capable of running a year between windings has a delicate mechanism and is very susceptible to vibration or knocks. The slightest sideways movement can stop a clock. **Always site anniversary clocks on a solid surface like a mantelpiece or shelf, never a table.**

Regulation

A number of factors affect the timekeeping of a clock (temperature, balance etc.). No matter how well a clock may have been overhauled, final adjustment is almost always necessary. A rotary pendulum has a fixed length, unlike a conventional clock. Although length does affect the timekeeping, adjustments are made by moving the balls or pendulum weights in and out. Ball type pendulums normally have a serrated adjustment nut and this is often marked 'Fast - Slow' or 'Advance - Retard'. This moves all the balls in and out simultaneously. Older clocks often had a flat disk pendulum with a pair of weights connected by a steel shaft. These are adjusted by rotating the shaft that connects them using a small key. This makes both weights move in and out simultaneously. **The further out the balls or weights, the slower the clock will run.**

Do not alter the pendulum more than once in 24 hours and remember that spring driven clocks may run slower as the spring unwinds. Keep a note of the amount of adjustment made and the resulting effect.

The reputation anniversary clocks have for poor timekeeping is generally unfair. Weekly wound clocks tend to be corrected weekly for any small loss or gain. Because anniversary clocks require no attention for months on end, the error accumulates unnoticed until it becomes unacceptable. A well regulated clock with a modern temperature compensating suspension should keep good time.

Never move a clock with the pendulum attached, as this will damage the delicate spring on which the pendulum is suspended and may cause expensive damage to the escapement.

Setting up

The pendulum

The variation in design of anniversary clocks makes it impossible to give precise instructions on all models, but they fall into two main categories:

Detachable pendulums: The pendulums of these older and simpler clocks are completely removed for transport. Very carefully fit the pendulum onto the brass block at the bottom of the suspension wire. If a suspension wire guard is fitted, then this sometimes has to be raised (by loosening any nuts or by friction alone) to get access to the bottom block. Never put any strain on the wire as you fit the pendulum. The hook normally goes up and over the pins projecting from the sides of the block. Ensure that the bottom of the pendulum fits within any guide on the base.

Attached pendulums: Later models have locking devices to allow the clock to be moved with the pendulum in place. Various methods have been used, but almost all involve levers that hold and release the pendulum securely. Gently release the lever.

Levelling

Later clocks have levelling screws. Adjust these until the pendulum hangs quite centrally. If no levelling screws are fitted, check the surface beneath the clock with a spirit level and ensure the pendulum hangs centrally. A poor but functional method of levelling is to use two small cardboard wedges under the base.

Starting and Stopping

Start by rotating the pendulum in either direction one complete turn from the stationary position and let go. It will rotate slightly faster than normal, but will gradually settle down to about 3/4 of a turn each way. Never turn the pendulum more than 1 1/2 turns*, as this may put a permanent twist in the wire, rendering it useless. To stop the clock, gently grasp the pendulum as it approaches the central position.

Exceptions:
Although known as anniversary clocks (the intention being to wind them on a particular anniversary each year), some models go for 1,000 days and at least one cheap model only goes for a month.
*Some very modern clocks rotate quickly, with up to 3 revolutions each way.

SETTING UP & REGULATING
ANNIVERSARY CLOCKS

It is essential a clock is 'set up' properly when put into operation after a move to a new position. No matter how thoroughly a clock is overhauled, if it does not receive this final attention it may suffer from loss of power and subsequently stop. Provided a clock is transported carefully with the pendulum removed or secured and subsequently placed on a firm level surface, no adjustment should be necessary.

Siting

A clock capable of running a year between windings has a delicate mechanism and is very susceptible to vibration or knocks. The slightest sideways movement can stop a clock. **Always site anniversary clocks on a solid surface like a mantelpiece or shelf, never a table.**

Regulation

A number of factors affect the timekeeping of a clock (temperature, balance etc.). No matter how well a clock may have been overhauled, final adjustment is almost always necessary. A rotary pendulum has a fixed length, unlike a conventional clock. Although length does affect the timekeeping, adjustments are made by moving the balls or pendulum weights in and out. Ball type pendulums normally have a serrated adjustment nut and this is often marked 'Fast - Slow' or 'Advance - Retard'. This moves all the balls in and out simultaneously. Older clocks often had a flat disk pendulum with a pair of weights connected by a steel shaft. These are adjusted by rotating the shaft that connects them using a small key. This makes both weights move in and out simultaneously. **The further out the balls or weights, the slower the clock will run.**

Do not alter the pendulum more than once in 24 hours and remember that spring driven clocks may run slower as the spring unwinds. Keep a note of the amount of adjustment made and the resulting effect.

The reputation anniversary clocks have for poor timekeeping is generally unfair. Weekly wound clocks tend to be corrected weekly for any small loss or gain. Because anniversary clocks require no attention for months on end, the error accumulates unnoticed until it becomes unacceptable. A well regulated clock with a modern temperature compensating suspension should keep good time.

Never move a clock with the pendulum attached, as this will damage the delicate spring on which the pendulum is suspended and may cause expensive damage to the escapement.

Setting up

The pendulum

The variation in design of anniversary clocks makes it impossible to give precise instructions on all models, but they fall into two main categories:

Detachable pendulums: The pendulums of these older and simpler clocks are completely removed for transport. Very carefully fit the pendulum onto the brass block at the bottom of the suspension wire. If a suspension wire guard is fitted, then this sometimes has to be raised (by loosening any nuts or by friction alone) to get access to the bottom block. Never put any strain on the wire as you fit the pendulum. The hook normally goes up and over the pins projecting from the sides of the block. Ensure that the bottom of the pendulum fits within any guide on the base.

Attached pendulums: Later models have locking devices to allow the clock to be moved with the pendulum in place. Various methods have been used, but almost all involve levers that hold and release the pendulum securely. Gently release the lever.

Levelling

Later clocks have levelling screws. Adjust these until the pendulum hangs quite centrally. If no levelling screws are fitted, check the surface beneath the clock with a spirit level and ensure the pendulum hangs centrally. A poor but functional method of levelling is to use two small cardboard wedges under the base.

Starting and Stopping

Start by rotating the pendulum in either direction one complete turn from the stationary position and let go. It will rotate slightly faster than normal, but will gradually settle down to about 3/4 of a turn each way. Never turn the pendulum more than 1 1/2 turns*, as this may put a permanent twist in the wire, rendering it useless. To stop the clock, gently grasp the pendulum as it approaches the central position.

Exceptions:
Although known as anniversary clocks (the intention being to wind them on a particular anniversary each year), some models go for 1,000 days and at least one cheap model only goes for a month.
*Some very modern clocks rotate quickly, with up to 3 revolutions each way.

Further supplies available from most clock material dealers or direct from
Meadows & Passmore Ltd. 1 Ellen Street Portslade Brighton East Sussex BN41 1EU
© Meadows & Passmore Ltd, 1997

Anniversary Clock Adjusting. Appendix/removable pages **XIII**

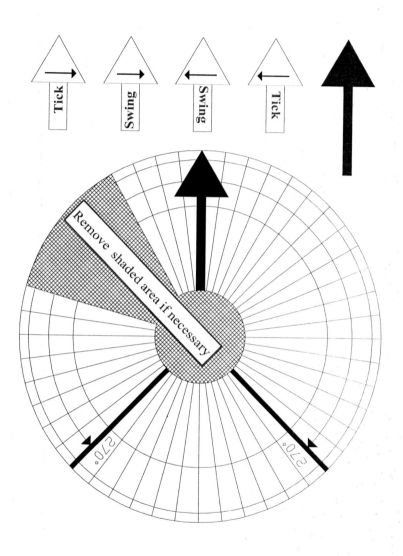

Adjusting scale. © Mervyn Passmore 2002

XIV   Anniversary Clock Adjusting Appendix/removable pages